AGENT MOOSE

WITH ART BY

Mo O'Hara   Jess Bradley

SCHOLASTIC

With love to my mom –
my biggest supporter and my friend.
–M.O.

For my wonderful boys, John-Paul and Jacob.
Love you silly guys.
–J.B.

Published in the UK by Scholastic, 2022
Euston House, 24 Eversholt Street, London, NW1 1DB
Scholastic Ireland, 89E Lagan Road, Dublin Industrial Estate, Glasnevin, Dublin, D11 HP5F

SCHOLASTIC and associated logos are trademarks and/or
registered trademarks of Scholastic Inc.

First published in the US by Feiwel and Friends, an imprint of
Macmillan Publishing Group, LLC, 2020

Text © Mo O'Hara, 2020
Illustrations © Jess Bradley, 2020

The right of Mo O'Hara and Jess Bradley to be identified as the author and illustrator of this work
has been asserted by them under the Copyright, Designs and Patents Act 1988.

ISBN 978 0702 31439 1

A CIP catalogue record for this book is available from the British Library.

Printed by C&C, China

1 3 5 7 9 10 8 6 4 2

www.scholastic.co.uk

Book design by Liz Dresner
Colour by John-Paul Bove
Lettering by Micah Meyer

MIX
Paper from
responsible sources
FSC
www.fsc.org   FSC® C008047

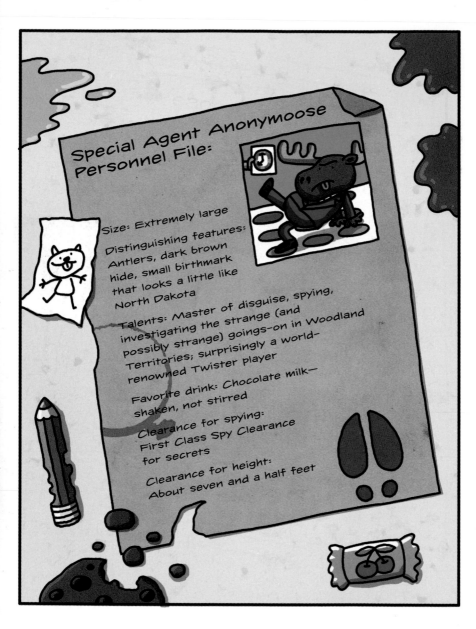

Math for fun!

$$\sqrt{4} \div 7 + 1.3946$$

$\times 8$

$=$

$\downarrow$

Carry
the
one

$=$

52

Not-Quite-So-Special Agent Owlfred Personnel File:

Size: Small enough that he can fit in a moose's pocket

Distinguishing features: Gray, feathery, can do that weird owl thing where they twist their head most of the way around (but it makes him slightly motion sick)

Talents: Very precise analysis of clues and data, calm attitude in a crisis, patience in a crisis (also very good at just avoiding a crisis)

Favorite drink: Hot cocoa with extra chocolate

Clearance for spying: Third Class Spy Clearance for secrets

Clearance for height: Irrelevant due to flying and all

To-Do List

• Hot chocolate (lots)

• Solve mystery

Chapter 1

★ NEWS OF THE WILD ★

MOOSE MISJUDGES MANIC MOON MAYHEM

"No COMMENT," SAID MOOSE.

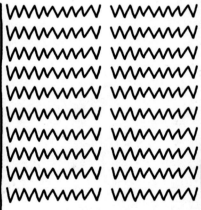

OCTOPUS WINS PRIZE

SHAKEN AND STIRRED

Anonymoose, I have your chocolate milk. Shaken, not stirred.

I'm going to be the laughing moose of the forest...

Ah, you've seen the morning paper, then?

I was so close, Owlfred. This would have been my 100th successfully solved case, you know.

Yes, it's a shame it didn't count, but the moon wasn't actually moon-napped.

It should have counted.

It wasn't technically a crime, sir. More of a meteorological event.

Grumble!

BIG FOREST NEWS

Mmmy mmave maa mery murgent message mrom...

Sorry, the message pod... I can't really understand...

Ptoo!

Phew, that's better. I have an urgent message from Woodland HQ—Special Branch.

Agent Moose, your mission is to investigate a missing animal—Terrance Turtle. He was a witness in the recent high-profile robbery case that your esteemed colleague and fellow agent Camo Chameleon just solved. It was his 100th case. We're throwing him a little party to celebrate down in South Shore where he's based.

SPECIAL BRANCH☆

We thought it would work out well. You could attend the party, congratulate Camo Chameleon on being the best agent at Woodland HQ, and then nip off and find this missing witness.

See you soon. Hey, it looks like someone is having a party. Is this for you, Anonymoose?

No, but it could have been if only the moon...

Just let it go, Anonymoose. Thank you, porpoises.

eye roll!

Do you hear something? It sounds like singing...

23

Mr. Chameleon, I'm Owlfred, Anonymoose's assistant. I just wanted to say I've read about all your past cases. You have such an impressive—

Yes, I do. Look, go see the flamingos. They can get you an autographed photo or something. I've got to prepare for tonight... Hang on... Wait, why are you here? Why is Anonymoose here?

Starstruck!

Brush!

Grumble!

Well, there's a case about a turtle...

Congratulations, Camo!

Did that coat rack just talk? Hang on. Seven foot, brown, furry...? Anonymoose?

Do doo da loo....!

Not now!!

!!!

But if you are on the case, Anonymoose, then I'm sure that turtle stands a fairly good chance of maybe being found.

Thanks for your confidence, Camo.

Now, you must excuse me. See you both at the party.

Chapter 3

BIRD'S-EYE VIEW

We were wondering if you knew anything about a turtle?

We know lots of turtles. There's Tuco the pink-bellied side-neck turtle.

"Ouch. Can you pass me the sunblock? I think I got a little too much sun on my belly."

Oh, and the slider turtle twins— Tom and Tanya...

"I bet you I can drop down that dune faster! No way! Eat my sand!! Whooooo heeee!"

Those kids. Always racing somewhere.

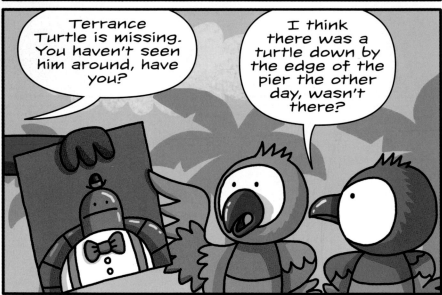

Ahhhhh!!

Ahhhhh! Ummm. Excuse me. Why are we doing this "Ahhhh" thing, Miss Mermaid?

Ahhhh! Sorry. I thought you were going to try to eat me.

Oh.

You're not going to try to eat me, are you?

I don't think so.

Good. Very good. Okay. So, I'm just going to sit here, then. Without shouting.

Okay.

  47

Ahhhhh!!

Like, I might wonder for instance...why is an owl floating on a billboard in the bay with his head through a mermaid poster?

You mean she's not a real mermaid?

He has feathers on his face. Do you know any mermaids with feathers on their face?

I don't know any mermaids, actually, so I was keeping an open mind.

Ahhhhh!!

Yes, me and Special Agent Moose.

Anonymoose. Lovely to make your acquaintance.

Ahhhhh!

Owlfred, you knew I was here.

I know. I just got in the "Ahhh" zone and it's hard to stop. Sorry.

Did that billboard just talk?

I'm a Special Agent, you see. Not actually a billboard.

This is a strange day.

Ahhhhh!!

Yes, quite.

So, do either of you know anything about a missing turtle?

Sometimes folks just disappear and are never seen again.

Ahhhhh!!

Enchanté.

What?

Enchanting to meet you?

Not enchanted

Even less enchanted

So, back to this missing turtle, then...

Ahhhhh!!

I think you two are better off just enjoying the sights around here. Not everyone likes someone sticking a beak into their business.

Glare!

Phew!

I thought ≥pant≥ they were going to ≥pant≥ eat me!

Both of them? Not likely. They did not want to talk turtle though. Hmmm. Definitely animals of...

interest.

Tropical punch, Mr. Chameleon?

Urk!

Now, I must get this ENORMOUS trophy polished for tonight. Beavers!!!

oof!~

Something is afoot...!

Sniff!

I'm not sure what is going on, but I definitely still smell foul play.

Hiccup! Sorry, that's me again. I just ate a message pod that I delivered to Camo Chameleon. Madam HQ wanted Camo to know that she will be here tonight to present the 100th case trophy to him herself.

So she is coming here? And we are no closer to solving the case of the missing turtle!

This Is a Strange Day

Chapter 6

GOOD OWL/BAD MOOSE

Now, I'm sure that this is where we last spotted him.

So, if you think that Barry is in on the turtle-napping, what makes you think that he won't just owl-nap me?

I suppose he could. Good point. Wait, shhh. I see something in the water.

Snip Snip!

Stop in the name of Agent Moose!! We need to question you on official Woodland HQ business.

Wait. You sound just like that billboard.

I am the billboard... I was the billboard... Never mind. I'm Anonymoose.

Good Owl/Bad Moose

Good Owl/Bad Moose

So, Barry, we want the facts about Terrance the Turtle.

BAD OWL! →

Well... I don't know him but I suppose he's a turtle... and his mother liked the name Terrance? Or maybe it was a family name, you know, like Barry. My mom hated the name Barry but my dad was a Barry Barracuda and his dad was a Barry Barracuda and his dad...

You mean you don't know anything about Terrance the Turtle's disappearance?

You're innocent?

Turtle-napped

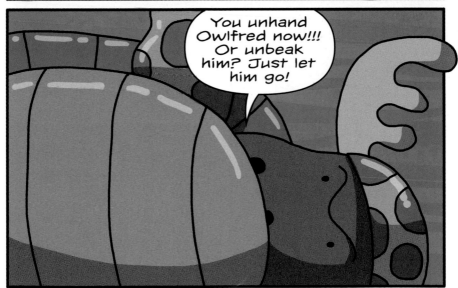

AGENT MOOSE

Still struggling!

Excuse me, Mr. Exceptionally Large Turtle? There was a moose asking us about a missing turtle earlier...

You wouldn't happen to be named Terrance, would you?

Turtle-napped

It's me, parrots! Anonymoose! I'm disguised as a turtle, and that pelican just turtle-napped Owlfred.

The coconut?

Yes, but he's an owl, and he was just turtle-napped.

Did you hit your head with all that rolling around?

Probably not. I need your help, parrots. And we need the message chipmunk and Newt the News Newt. I need to foil the pelican's plans and save Owlfred and hopefully Terrance.

Do we have to be dressed as coconuts for that?

He did it because he not only *solved* all the crimes. He *caused* all the crimes so he could get credit for solving them.

What a scoop!

You talk too much, little turtle. That's why I had to pouch you in the first place!

You caused the crimes?

Oh, yes, I forgot to say I recorded your whole confession on parrot-a-phone. In stereo!

"Gobble them up in your pouch, Paula! We can't have any loose ends."

"I can't have anyone finding out that I caused the very crimes I solved!!"

GASP!

Gulp!

To think we trusted you, Camo Chameleon. You are hereby stripped of the title Special Agent.

And you won't be getting any trophies anytime soon. Unless they give some sort of trophy for best behaved prisoner or something in Woodland Prison. But I really doubt you would win.

Hup!

Smack!

This is big news! Let me get a photo for *News of the Wild?*

Oh, I'll get out of the way so you can get a good pic of Anonymoose.

Not a chance, Owlfred. You were very brave. You should be front and center.

Click!

You both did your duty in a time of extreme pressure.

And you found your missing witness and helped to save him.

Very nice to be saved. It was getting very smelly in that pelican pouch.

Everyone who helped deserves a special thanks from Woodland HQ. Actually, Anonymoose, this means you have just solved your 100th case after all.

I can see the headlines now!

scribble!

100 cases! I knew you could do it, Anonymoose.

WE could do it. And now I think we have a party to go to!

Can I come?

For successfully solving your 100th case.

Gasp!

100 cases Solved

I had some help from my trusty Not-Quite-So-Special Agent Owlfred and the team from the Big Woods.

Proud!

We got together and wrote a little song to celebrate... Five, six, seven eight... Who's the moose with the most? Raise your glasses! Make a toast! Thanks are due. Yes, to you. And your funky woodland crew! You can stay on South Shore. And we'll sing to you some more. But we know, you must go. Find the chameleon...named...Ca...mo!!

OOHHHH YEAAAH!

Tap!

★ NEWS OF THE WILD ★

SLEEPY SOUTH SHORE SHOCKED by CALAMITOUS CHAMELEON CAPERS in MEGA MOOSE MYSTERY

HERO MOOSE! Plus Owl
wwwwwwwwww

WANTED!   WANTED!

BREAKING NEWS! Camo Chameleon at large! (Even though he's very small!) wwwwwwwwww
wwwwwwwww wwwwwwww
wwwwwwwww

"I'm glad the moose solved the crime but overall, I think I still like chocolate mousse better. You don't happen to have any, do you? In the shiny gold wrappers?"
Barry the Barracuda.
Chocolate Mousse not available for comment.

The Moose with the Most

 125

THANK YOU FOR READING.

The Friends who made

possible are:

Jean Feiwel, Publisher

Liz Szabla, Associate Publisher

Rich Deas, Senior Creative Director

Holly West, Senior Editor

Anna Roberto, Senior Editor

Kat Brzozowski, Senior Editor

Erin Siu, Associate Editor

Rachel Diebel, Assistant Editor

Emily Settle, Associate Editor

Foyinsi Adegbonmire, Editorial Assistant

Kim Waymer, Senior Production Manager

Liz Dresner, Associate Art Director

Mandy Veloso, Senior Production Editor